Wilma's mum had a charm bracelet. It was made of gold. The bracelet had ten charms on it. The charms were made of gold too.

"It's a beautiful bracelet," said Chip.

1

Wilma's mum was washing her hands at
the sink. She had the bracelet on. One of
the charms fell off the bracelet, and it went
down the plug hole.

Wilma's mum was very upset.

"I hope I can get the charm out of the plug hole," she said.

Chip ran and got his mum.

"She can get the charm out," he said.

Mum put a plastic bowl under the sink.
Everyone looked in the bowl.

"There's the charm," said Mum.

"Yuk!" said Wilma. "It's got dirt on it."

Wilma's mum was glad to get it back.

Mum found something else.

"Yuk!" she said. "Look what I've found."
It was Wilf's old chewing gum.

"What a place to stick old chewing
gum!" said Wilma's mum.

The children went to Biff's bedroom. Wilf had three packets of chewing gum. He gave some gum to Chip.

"This is my bedroom," said Biff, "so mind where you put the old chewing gum."

Suddenly the magic key began to glow. The magic took the children on a new adventure.

"Help!" said Wilf. "I don't know what to do with my old chewing gum."

The magic took the children back in time. It took them to a river. A boy and a girl were looking for something in the water.

The boy and the girl had big pans. They
scooped up little stones from the river.
Then they looked for tiny bits of gold in
the bottom of the pans.

The boy and girl got angry when they saw the children. They didn't want them to look for gold.

"This is our bit of river," they shouted. "Go and look for gold somewhere else!"

Wilf gave the boy and girl some gum.
They hadn't seen chewing gum before.
They didn't know what to do with it.

"You just chew it," said Wilf. "Chew it,
but don't swallow it."

The boy was called Luke and the girl
was called Alice. They lived in a hut by the
river. Alice and Luke looked for gold every
day. It was a hard life.

The family hadn't found any gold, and Luke and Alice were always hungry.

"Looking for gold is hard," said Luke. "Do you want to help us?"

The children helped look for gold. Wilf
and Biff helped Luke's father. Wilma and
Chip helped Alice and Luke.

"I'm glad I brought the gum," said Wilf.
"This is hard work."

It was cold in the river, and the children soon got tired.

"We do this every day," said Luke, "and we still haven't found any gold."

Suddenly, Luke's father shouted.

"Gold!" he yelled. "We've found gold."
He picked up a big nugget of gold and
jumped up and down. Everyone ran to see.

Everyone looked at the gold nugget. It felt heavy and cold.

"Hooray!" shouted Luke's mother. "We have found gold at last," she said. "I thought we'd never find any."

The children went to town with Luke's
mother and father. Luke and Alice were
excited.

"We can sell the gold," they said, "and
we can buy some food."

"We can buy new clothes," said Luke's
mother.

"And a new spade," said Luke's father.

"And some chewing gum," said Luke.

"What's chewing gum?" asked Luke's
father.

Some men were waiting in the road.

"Oh no!" said Luke's father. "Robbers!
They will steal our gold nugget. What shall
we do?"

Wilf had an idea. He spoke to all the children.

"Give me your chewing gum," he said. "Give me all the old chewing gum, and give me the gold nugget."

The robbers wanted gold and money.
"But we're just a poor family," said
Luke's father. "We haven't got any money
and we haven't found any gold."

The robbers looked everywhere. They searched everyone.

"We're only children," said Alice. "We haven't got any gold and we haven't got any money."

The robbers couldn't find the gold. They
let everyone go.

"Hooray," said Luke. "Wilf's chewing
gum saved the gold."

"Is *that* chewing gum?" asked Luke's
father.

Luke's father and mother got some
money for the gold.

"I can have a new dress," said Alice.

"And I can have new boots," said Luke.

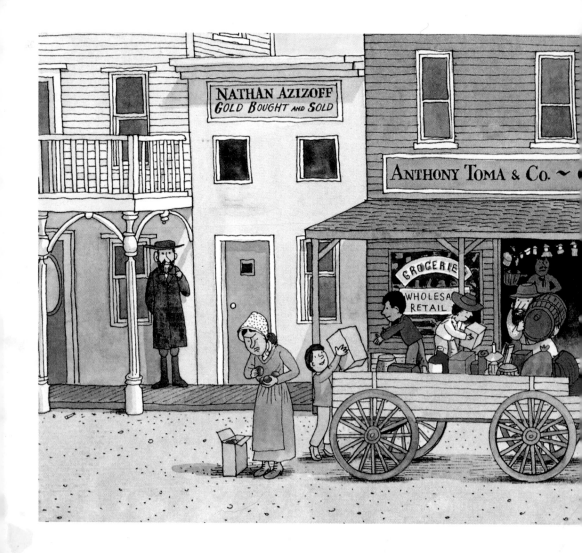

Luke's father bought a new cart. It was bigger than the old one.

"We need a new cart," said Luke. "There is so much to take home."

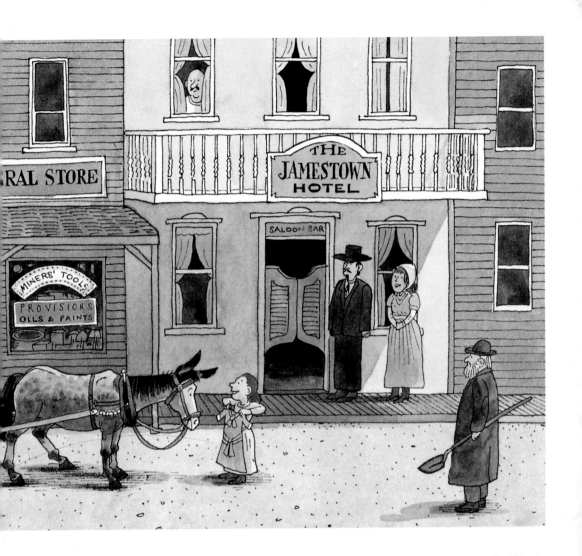

The children helped them put everything on the cart.

"This is hard work too," said Biff. "These magic adventures are not all fun."

They all went back to the river. The
family put on the new clothes. Wilma and
Biff looked for gold.

"I hope we find some," said Wilma. "I'd
love to find a gold nugget."

Suddenly, Biff saw a little yellow speck
in the pan. She had found some gold.
"It's very small," she said.
Just then, the magic key began to glow.

The magic took the children home. Biff looked at the gold.

"It looks really tiny, now," she said. "It looks like a speck of dust!"
Suddenly, Chip sneezed.

The speck of gold blew out of Biff's hand. It blew on to the carpet.

"Did you see where it went?" asked Biff.

"Oh no! Sorry!" said Chip.

the children

The children looked and looked. They couldn't find the little speck of gold.

"I don't think we ever will," said Biff.

"Oh no!" said everyone.

will
no said
oh